What Can I See?
¿Qué veo?

by Deborah Schecter

No part of this publication can be reproduced in whole or in part, or stored in a retrieval system, or transmitted in any form or by any means, electronic, mechanical, photocopying, recording, or otherwise, without written permission of the publisher. For permission, write to Scholastic Inc., 557 Broadway, New York, NY 10012.

ISBN: 978-1-338-70281-1
Illustrated by Anne Kennedy
Copyright © 2020 by Deborah Schecter. All rights reserved.
Published by Scholastic Inc., 557 Broadway, New York, NY 10012

10 9 8 7 6   68   23 24 25 26/0

Printed in Jiaxing, China. First printing, June 2020.

SCHOLASTIC

I see an ant.

Veo una hormiga.

I see a stone.

Veo una piedra.

I see a leaf.

Veo una hoja.

I see a home.

Veo una casa.

I see a bee.

Veo una abeja.

I see a flower.

Veo una flor.

But no one can see me!

¡Pero nadie puede verme!